The **Graham Kendrick**
Prayer Song Collection

We hope you enjoy *The Graham Kendrick Prayer Song Collection.*
Further copies are available
from your local Kevin Mayhew stockist.

In case of difficulty, or to request a catalogue,
please contact the publisher direct by writing to:

The Sales Department
WORLD WIDE WORSHIP
Buxhall
Stowmarket
Suffolk IP14 3BW

Phone 01449 737978
Fax 01449 737834
E-mail info@kevinmayhewltd.com

This collection features songs drawn from classic Kendrick albums including
Shine Jesus Shine, Is Anyone Thirsty? and *Illuminations.*

First published in Great Britain in 2002 by world wide worship.

© Copyright 2002 world wide worship.

ISBN 1 84003 862 4
ISMN M 57004 987 5
Catalogue No: 1400313

0 1 2 3 4 5 6 7 8 9

Cover design by Angela Selfe

Printed and bound in Great Britain

Important Copyright Information

The Publishers wish to express their gratitude to the copyright owners who have granted permission to include their copyright material in this book. Full details are indicated on the respective pages.

The **words** of most of the songs in this publication are covered by a **Church Copyright Licence** which is available from Christian Copyright Licensing International. This allows local church reproduction on overhead projector acetates, in service bulletins, songsheets, audio/visual recording and other formats.

The **music** in this book is covered by the additional **Music Reproduction Licence** which is issued by CCLI in the territories of Europe and Australasia. You may photocopy the music and words of the songs in the book provided:

You hold a current Music Reproduction Licence from CCLI.

The copyright owner of the song you intend to photocopy is included in the Authorised Catalogue List which comes with your Music Reproduction Licence.

The Music Reproduction Licence is **not** currently available in the USA or Canada.

Full details of CCLI can be obtained from their Web site (www.ccli.com) or you can contact them direct at the following offices:

Christian Copyright Licensing (Europe) Ltd
PO Box 1339, Eastbourne, East Sussex, BN21 1AD, UK
Tel: +44 (0)1323 417711; Fax: +44 (0)1323 417722; E-mail: info@ccli.co.uk

CCL Asia-Pacific Pty Ltd (Australia and New Zealand)
PO Box 6644, Baulkham Hills Business Centre, NSW 2153, Australia
Tel: +61 (02) 9894-5386; Toll Free Phone: 1-800-635-474
Fax: +61 (02) 9894-5701; Toll Free Fax: 1-800-244-477
E-mail executive@ccli.co.au

Christian Copyright Licensing Inc
17201 NE Sacramento Street, Portland, Oregon 97230, USA
Tel: +1 (503) 257 2230; Toll Free Phone: 1 (800) 234 2446;
Fax: +1 (503) 257 2244; E-mail executive@ccli.com

Please note, all texts and music in this book are protected by copyright and if you do <u>not</u> possess a licence from CCLI they may <u>not</u> be reproduced in any way for sale or private use without the consent of the copyright owner.

Foreword

The more we worship God the more the things that concern him become our concerns and we find ourselves interceding. The dynamic is a simple one, the more we love God the more we want his will done on earth as in heaven. It is not surprising then that worshippers find praise and adoration flow into intercession. These songs have been written to facilitate these times when sung worship becomes sung prayer and in particular when there is a desire to pray for the neighbourhood, the city and the nation. Many of them have been used on the streets around the world as well as in church services and prayer meetings. In this selection the mood ranges from confident proclamation to lament and reflection. The instruments too have their voice as the musicians express their God-given longings for the love of God to flow. I hope that these songs continue to be a resource for praying churches as well as for personal devotions.

GRAHAM KENDRICK

CONTENTS

1 Come, let us worship Jesus

King of the nations

Words and Music: Graham Kendrick

2. Lavish our heart's affection,
   deepest love and highest praise.
   Voice, race and language blending,
   all the world amazed.

4. Come, Lord, and fill your temple,
   glorify your dwelling-place,
   till nations see your splendour
   and seek your face.

3. Bring tributes from the nations,
   come in joyful cavalcades.
   One thund'rous acclamation,
   one banner raised.

5. Fear God and give him glory,
   for his hour of judgement comes.
   Creator, Lord Almighty,
   worship him alone.

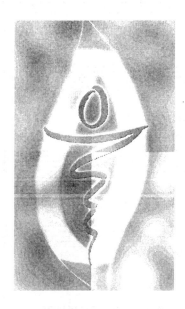

2 Hear, O Lord, our cry

Revive us again

Words and Music: Graham Kendrick

2. Hear, O Lord, our cry:
   revive us, revive us again.
   For the sake of the children
   revive us, revive us again.
   Lord, hear our cry.
   Lord, hear our cry.

3 Hear our cry

Words and Music: Graham Kendrick

(Women) Hear our cry, O hear our cry: 'Je - sus, come!' (Men) Hear our cry, O (Women)

hear our cry: (Men) 'Je - sus, come!'

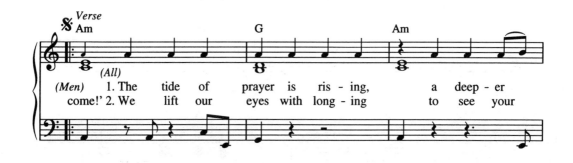

Verse

(Men) 1. The tide of prayer is ris - ing, a deep - er
come!' 2. We lift our eyes with long - ing to see your

pas - sion burn - ing —
king - dom com - ing — (Women) Hear our cry, O hear our cry: (Men) 'Je - sus,

3. The streets of teeming cities
   cry out for healing rivers –

4. Refresh them with your presence,
   give grace for deep repentance –

5. Tear back the shroud of shadows
   that covers all the peoples –

6. Revealing your salvation
   in ev'ry tribe and nation –

4 If my people who bear my name

Words and Music: Graham Kendrick

If my peo - ple who bear my name will hum - ble them-selves and

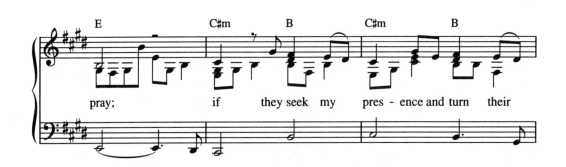

pray; if they seek my pres - ence and turn their

backs on their wick-ed ways. Then I will hear from

hea - ven, I'll hear from hea - ven and will for - give,

I will for-give their sins and will heal their land, yes I will

heal their land.

5 Let it fill the room

Words and Music: Graham Kendrick

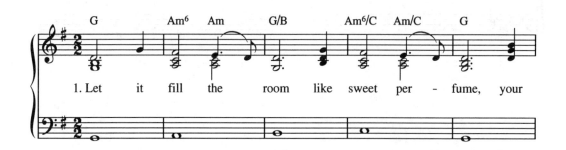

1. Let it fill the room like sweet per - fume, your

pre - sence here. Let each heart be

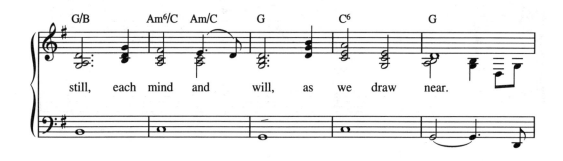

still, each mind and will, as we draw near.

We have tas - ted of your good - ness,

that is why we say: fill this cup, Lord,

fill us up with more, much more of

you.

2. Let my spirit breathe
   the love you give; so bountiful.
   Love that heals the pain,
   that takes the shame
   and calms our fear.
   Overflow me, overwhelm me,
   never let me go.
   Here's my cup, Lord,
   fill me up with more,
   much more of you.

6 Lord, have mercy

Prayer song

Words and Music: Graham Kendrick

Leader: Lord, our hearts overflow with thankfulness and praise for your amazing love and tender
mercy. Yet there are countless millions for whom you died, who know nothing of your love.
All: O God of mercy, forgive us our neglect, awaken your church in purity and power,
and make us an instrument of extraordinary blessing, right here and throughout this land!

2. **B♭**   **C**   **Gm**
    A   **B**   **F♯m**

on us.   2. Send your
              3. Save the

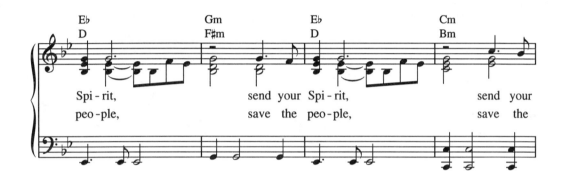

E♭   **Gm**   **E♭**   **Cm**
D   **F♯m**   **D**   **Bm**

Spi - rit,   send your Spi - rit,   send your
peo -ple,   save the peo - ple,   save the

Dm   **C**   *1.*   *2.*
C♯m   **B**

Spi - rit   on us.
peo - ple,   O Lord.   O

D   **C**   **D**
C♯   **B**   **C♯**

Lord,   O Lord.

7 Love of Christ, come now

Words and Music: Graham Kendrick

8 O Lord, the clouds are gathering

Words and Music: Graham Kendrick

2. O Lord, over the nations now,
   where is the dove of peace?
   Her wings are broken.
   O Lord, while precious children starve,
   the tools of war increase;
   their bread is stolen.

3. O Lord, dark pow'rs are poised to flood
   our streets with hate and fear;
   we must awaken!
   O Lord, let love reclaim the lives
   that sin would sweep away,
   and let your kingdom come.

4. Yet, O Lord, your glorious cross shall tower
   triumphant in this land,
   evil confounding.
   Through the fire your suffering church displays
   the glories of her Christ:
   praises resounding.

9 Peace be to these streets

Words and Music: Graham Kendrick

1. & 2. Peace be to these streets, peace be to these streets,

peace be to these streets in the name of Je - sus.

Chorus

Walk here, Lord, draw near, Lord, pass through these

streets to - day. Bring heal - ing, for - give - ness;

here let your liv - ing wa - ters flow.

Last time

Peace be to these streets!

3. Love come to these streets,
   love come to these streets,
   love come to these streets in the name of Jesus.

4. Joy come to these streets,
   joy come to these streets,
   joy come to these streets in the name of Jesus.

10 Save the people

Words and Music: Graham Kendrick

save the peo - ple now.

2. Save the children, save the children now. *(x4)*
   Lord, have mercy. Christ, have mercy.
   Father, hear our prayer: save the children now.

3. Send your Spirit, send your Spirit now. *(x4)*
   Lord, have mercy. Christ, have mercy.
   Father, hear our prayer: send your Spirit now.

4. Send revival, send revival now. *(x4)*
   Lord, have mercy. Christ, have mercy.
   Father, hear our prayer: send revival now.

   Add extra verses as required, for example:
   Send the fire . . .
   Save the nation . . .

11 Soften my heart, Lord

Words and Music: Graham Kendrick

12 Turn our hearts

Words and Music: Graham Kendrick

Turn our hearts, turn our

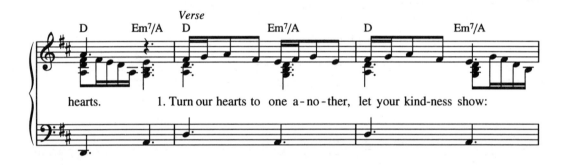

hearts. 1. Turn our hearts to one a-no-ther, let your kind-ness show:

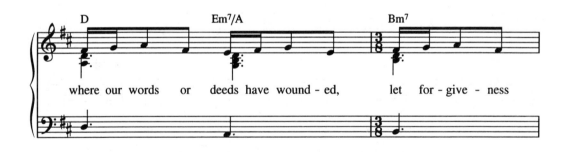

where our words or deeds have wound-ed, let for-give-ness

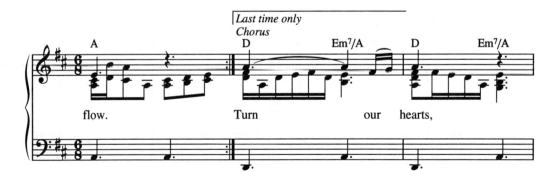

flow. Turn our hearts,

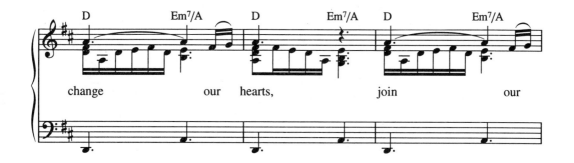

change   our   hearts,   join   our

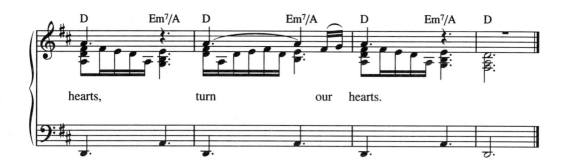

hearts,   turn   our   hearts.

2. Turn our hearts from pride and anger
to your ways of peace,
for you died and shed your blood
that enmity may cease.

3. Turn the hearts of generations
that we may be one:
make us partners in the kingdom
till your work is done.

4. As we all have been forgiven,
so must we forgive;
as we all have found acceptance,
so let us receive.

13 Turn to me and be saved

Words and Music: Graham Kendrick

2.

D	Asus⁴/E	A	E	C♯⁷	F♯m	E
C	Gsus⁴/D	G	D	B⁷	Em	D

o-ther.   For you are God,   and there is   no

D	Asus⁴/E	A	E	C♯⁷	F♯m	E
C	Gsus⁴/D	G	D	B⁷	Em	D

o - ther.   For you are God,   and there is   no

F♯m / Em   *All sing own prayers*   *12 times*   E⁶/F♯ / D⁶/E

o - ther.

SHOUT

Leader	Now, Lord, send your Holy Spirit.
All	Now, Lord, send your Holy Spirit.
Leader	Drench this land with your awesome presence.
All	Drench this land with your awesome presence.
Leader	Send your Holy Spirit more powerfully.
All	Send your Holy Spirit more powerfully.
Leader	Let grace and mercy flood this land.
All	Let grace and mercy flood this land.
Leader	Let mercy triumph over judgement.
All	Let mercy triumph over judgement.
Leader	Let mercy triumph over judgement.
All	Let mercy triumph over judgement.

14 Where two or three

Words and Music: Graham Kendrick

15 Who can sound the depths of sorrow

Words and Music: Graham Kendrick

up - on our na - tion, up - on our na - tion have

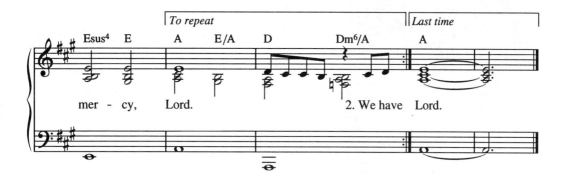

mer - cy, Lord. 2. We have Lord.

2. We have scorned the truth you gave us,
   we have bowed to other lords.
   We have sacrificed the children
   on the altar of our gods.
   O let truth again shine on us,
   let your holy fear descend:
   upon our nation, upon our nation
   have mercy, Lord.

(Men)
3. Who can stand before your anger?
   Who can face your piercing eyes?
   For you love the weak and helpless,
   and you hear the victims' cries.
   (All)
   Yes, you are a God of justice,
   and your judgement surely comes:
   upon our nation, upon our nation
   have mercy, Lord.

(Women)
4. Who will stand against the violence?
   Who will comfort those who mourn?
   In an age of cruel rejection,
   who will build for love a home?
   (All)
   Come and shake us into action,
   come and melt our hearts of stone:
   upon your people, upon your people
   have mercy, Lord.

5. Who can sound the depths of mercy
   in the Father heart of God?
   For there is a Man of sorrows
   who for sinners shed his blood.
   He can heal the wounds of nations,
   he can wash the guilty clean:
   because of Jesus, because of Jesus
   have mercy, Lord.

Note: some congregations may wish to add to the effectiveness of this song by
transposing the final verse up a semitone, into B♭ major.

The **Graham Kendrick**
Psalm Collection
Book, CD & Cassette

Book: 1400312
ISMN M 57004 988 2

CD: 1490089
Cassette: 1480088

An inspiring collection of 15 songs which have their origin in the Psalms. This selection is joyful and uplifting with an emphasis on proclaiming hope for the world, transformation and unity through the power of God's love.

An excellent resource for praying churches as well as for personal devotions.

- *Christ is King of all creation*
- *Declare his glory*
- *Far and near (Say it loud)*
- *From where the sun rises*
- *God, be gracious*
- *God is great*
- *How good and how pleasant*
- *Lift up your heads (O you gates)*
- *Lord, we come in your name (Join our hearts)*
- *My heart is full (All the glory)*
- *Open the gates*
- *Sing a new song (Psalm 149)*
- *To you, O Lord, I lift up my soul*
- *Welcome the King*
- *When the Lord brought us back (Psalm 126)*

Also available:

The **Graham Kendrick** Prayer Song Collection *CD & Cassette*

CD: 1490088
Cassette: 1480087

Featuring all of his worship songs from this book:

- *Come, let us worship Jesus (King of the nations)*
- *Hear, O Lord, our cry (Revive us again)*
- *Hear our cry*
- *If my people who bear my name*
- *Let it fill the room*
- *Lord, have mercy (Prayer song)*
- *Love of Christ, come now*
- *O Lord, the clouds are gathering*
- *Peace be to these streets*
- *Save the people*
- *Soften my heart, Lord*
- *Turn our hearts*
- *Turn to me and be saved*
- *Where two or three*
- *Who can sound the depths of sorrow*